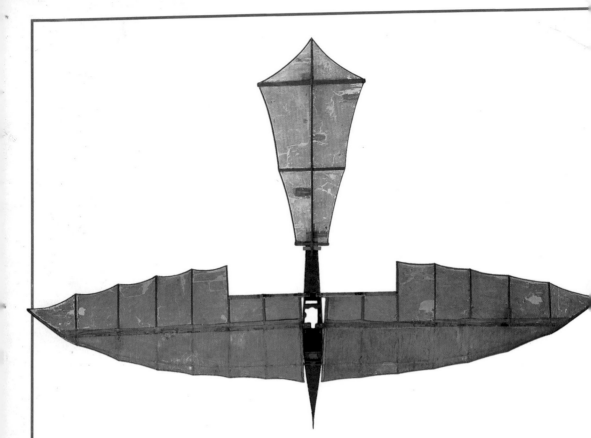

SNAP
SHOT

Art director Roger Priddy
Editor Mary Ling
Designers David Gillingwater
Sharon Grant

Special photography
Dave King, Peter Anderson, Martin Cameron,
Andy Crawford, Steve Gorton, Tim Ridley,
James Stevenson and Mike Dunning

A Dorling Kindersley Book

First published in Great Britain in 1994
by Snapshot™, an imprint of Covent Garden Book
9 Henrietta Street, London, WC2E 8PS

A CIP catalogue record for this book is
available from the British Library
ISBN 1-85948-013-6

Colour reproduction by Colourscan
Printed in Belgium by Proost

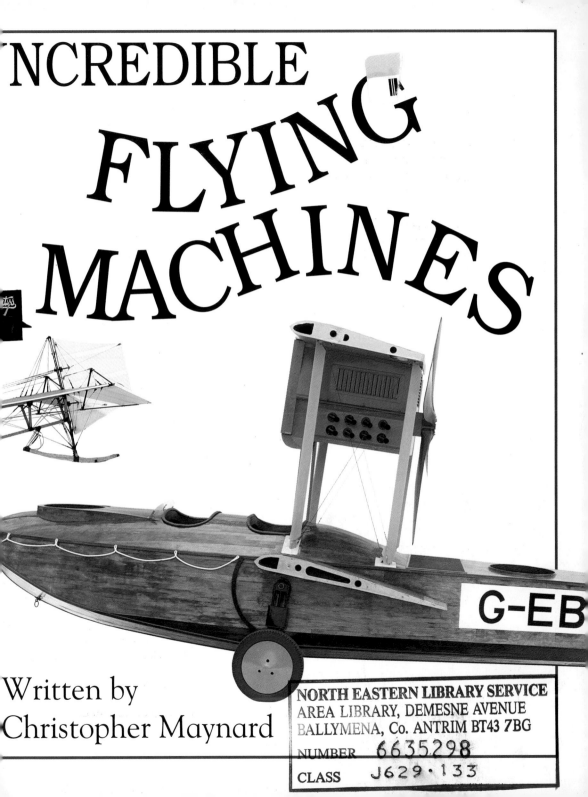

INCREDIBLE

FLYING
MACHINES

G-EB

Written by
Christopher Maynard

Contents

Bell 47G-3B1

4

Harrier
jump jet

Flap flop

People once thought they could build sets of wings and fly just by flapping them. But this always ended in a flop.

A steam engine

Even flapping arms and legs never worked

Leonardo da Vinci's orthinopter

Flap doodle

Hundreds of years ago, Leonardo da Vinci drew up plans for a fantastic flapping machine. But it would never have risen off the ground.

Wooden pedals pushed by legs

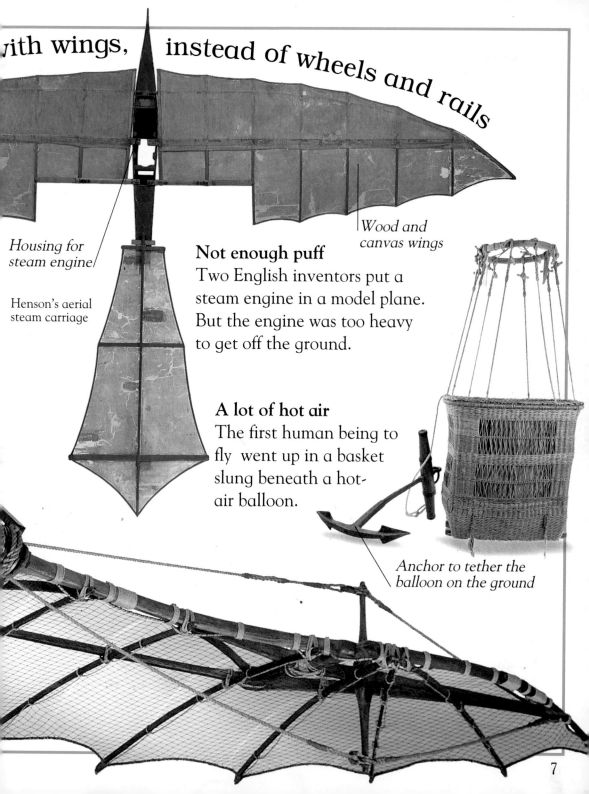

Wood and canvas wings

Housing for steam engine

Henson's aerial steam carriage

Not enough puff
Two English inventors put a steam engine in a model plane. But the engine was too heavy to get off the ground.

A lot of hot air
The first human being to fly went up in a basket slung beneath a hot-air balloon.

Anchor to tether the balloon on the ground

7

Up and away

Balloons can float, gliders can glide, but planes can fly only if they have powerful motors.

Cotton fabric

Avro triplane IV

Wright brothers' "Flyer"

How many wings in a triplane?

First flight
The Wright brothers w the first pilots to fly a plane with a motor.

Wing, wing, wing!
Early planes were made stronger by having two or even three sets of wings.

Wooden strut

Why were wings wired?
When wings were wooden, they
needed strong wires to hold them
in place, or they would fall off.

Deperdussin
monoplane

A plane with one set of wings ...
is called a monoplane

Taut fabric

Take that!

Planes first began shooting at each other and dropping bombs during World War I. They were useful for spying on the enemy, too.

Machine-gun

L.V.G. C.VI
7198/18

4503   4503

Wet, windy, and very, very cold

Warm fold up collar

Soft "chrome" leather

Dressed to kill
Sitting out in the open, pilots needed extra-thick clothes to keep them from freezing.

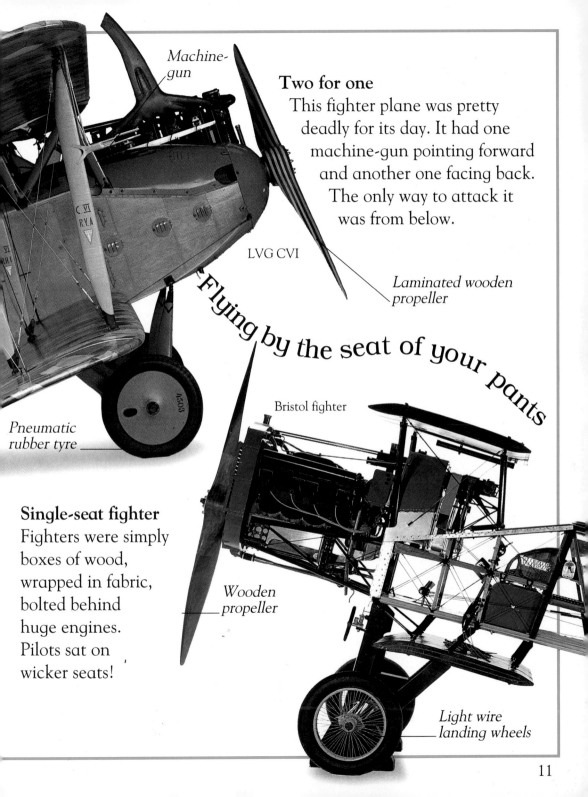

Machine-gun

Two for one

This fighter plane was pretty deadly for its day. It had one machine-gun pointing forward and another one facing back. The only way to attack it was from below.

LVG CVI

Laminated wooden propeller

Flying by the seat of your pants

Bristol fighter

Pneumatic rubber tyre

Single-seat fighter

Fighters were simply boxes of wood, wrapped in fabric, bolted behind huge engines. Pilots sat on wicker seats!

Wooden propeller

Light wire landing wheels

11

Sky buses

Modern passenger planes are made out of aluminium, a metal that is very strong, but very ligh

Fly in the nose
Pilots usually fly up front in the nose-section, or cockpit, of passenger planes.

Lockheed Electra

Small and fast ...

Metal exterior

Fast and high
The Electra could fly over 300 km/h (180 mph), which was much faster than wood and fabric planes.

Big push
Really big passenger planes have engines powerful enough to take them almost halfway round the world.

Around the world ... in no time

Boeing 747
Jumbo Jet

Hundreds and thousands
A big jumbo jet can carry about 400 people at a time on a single hop of some 12,000 kilometres (7,200 miles).

smooth and streamlined

Rudder

Swivelling rubber-tyred tail wheel

NC5171N

Water birds

Seaplanes and flying boats are planes that can land and take off on water. This is especially useful when there are no runways around!

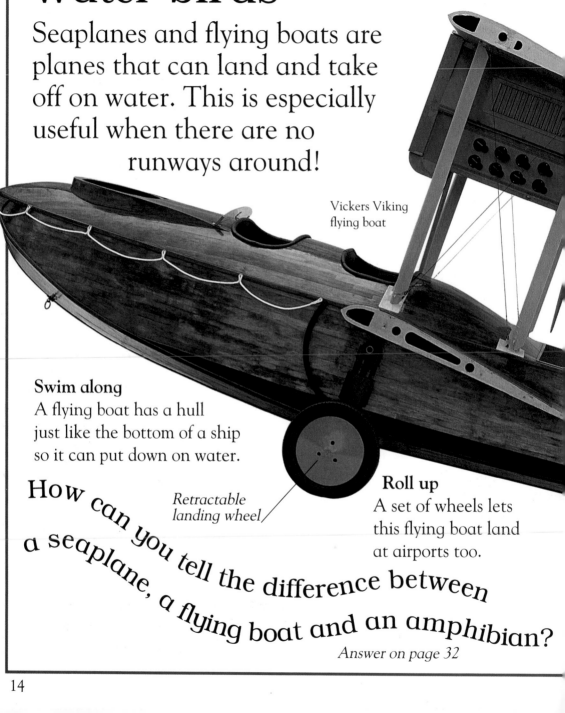

Vickers Viking flying boat

Swim along
A flying boat has a hull just like the bottom of a ship so it can put down on water.

Retractable landing wheel

Roll up
A set of wheels lets this flying boat land at airports too.

How can you tell the difference between a seaplane, a flying boat and an amphibian?

Answer on page 32

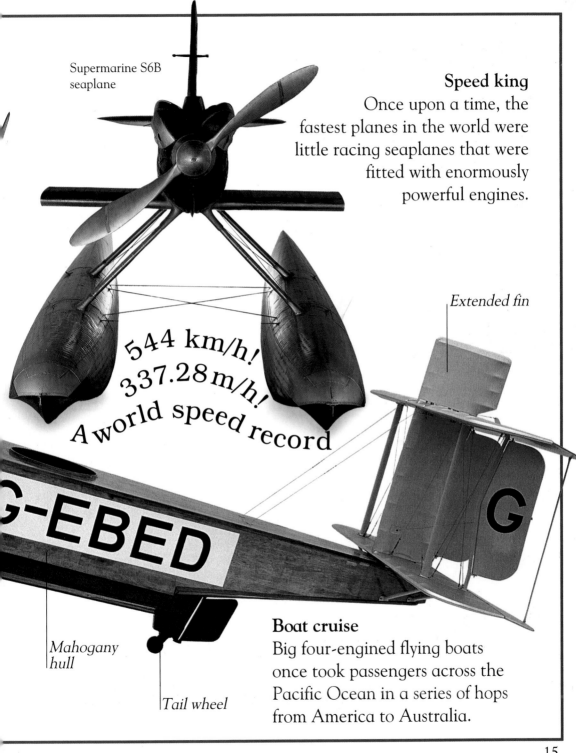

Supermarine S6B
seaplane

Speed king
Once upon a time, the
fastest planes in the world were
little racing seaplanes that were
fitted with enormously
powerful engines.

544 km/h!
337.28 m/h!
A world speed record

Extended fin

G-EBED

G

*Mahogany
hull*

Tail wheel

Boat cruise
Big four-engined flying boats
once took passengers across the
Pacific Ocean in a series of hops
from America to Australia.

Whirly birds

Helicopters are the humming-birds of the plane world. Their rotor blades are like thin wings. As the blades whirl, they lift the helicopter into the air.

Look ma! No wings
An autogiro has whirling blades to lift it, and a big propeller to drive it forward.

Autogiro propeller

Twin-blade main rotor

Cierva C-30 autogiro

K4232

A strange machine that's half helicopter, half plane

Plastic canopy

Main rotor blade

Westland
Sea King

The flying goldfish bowl

Rescue me!
A helicopter can
hover in one spot
to let down a line
and pull stranded
people up to safety.

See plane
The pilot rides
inside a bubble
cabin of clear
plastic so it
is possible to
see in almost
every direction.

Bell 47G-3B1

Jump jet

Helicopters are not the
only flying machines that
take off and land straight up
and down. The Harrier jump jet
is a VTOL (vertical take off and
landing). It rotates four powerful
jet nozzles downwards to lift
off vertically or hover
like a hawk.

The plane that takes off like a lift

Go forward
Four nozzles at the
back of the Harrier's
powerful jet engine
point to the rear when
it flies fast and low.

Front nozzle

Disposable fuel tanks

Hydraulically steered nose gear

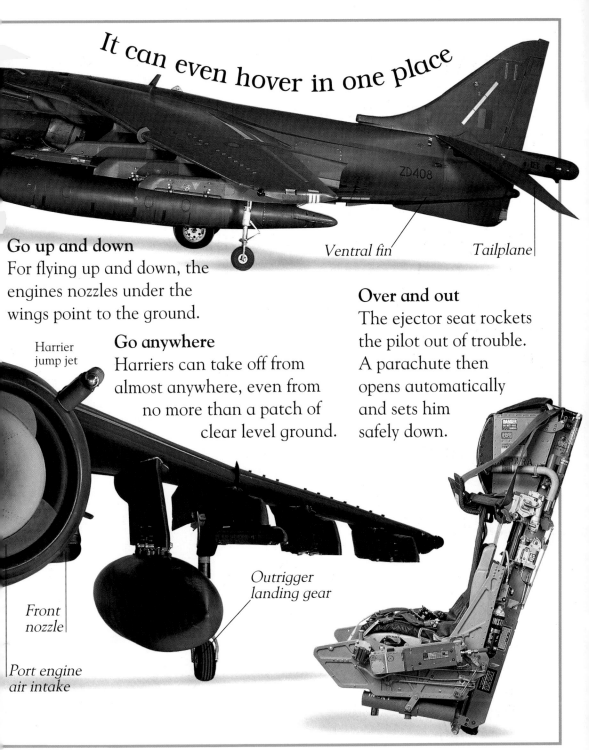

It can even hover in one place

ZD408

Ventral fin   Tailplane

Go up and down

For flying up and down, the engines nozzles under the wings point to the ground.

Harrier jump jet

Go anywhere

Harriers can take off from almost anywhere, even from no more than a patch of clear level ground.

Over and out

The ejector seat rockets the pilot out of trouble. A parachute then opens automatically and sets him safely down.

Outrigger landing gear

Front nozzle

Port engine air intake

Fighting jets

Fighter planes today are so fast
and powerful that pilots need the
help of computers in order to fly them.

Pilots up front, navigators in back

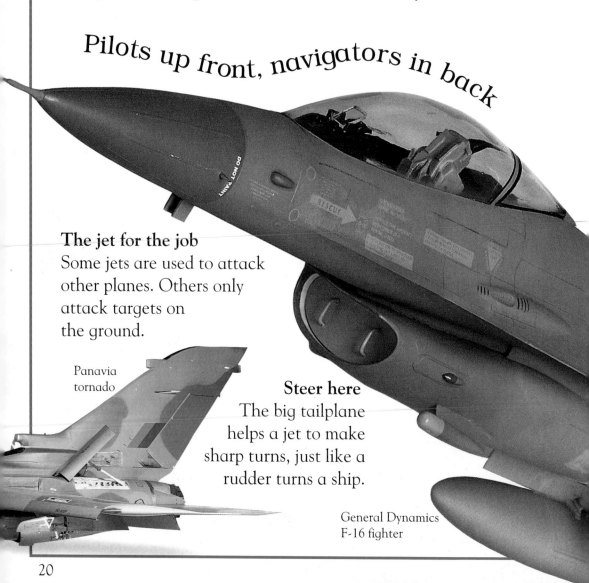

The jet for the job
Some jets are used to attack
other planes. Others only
attack targets on
the ground.

Panavia
tornado

Steer here
The big tailplane
helps a jet to make
sharp turns, just like a
rudder turns a ship.

General Dynamics
F-16 fighter

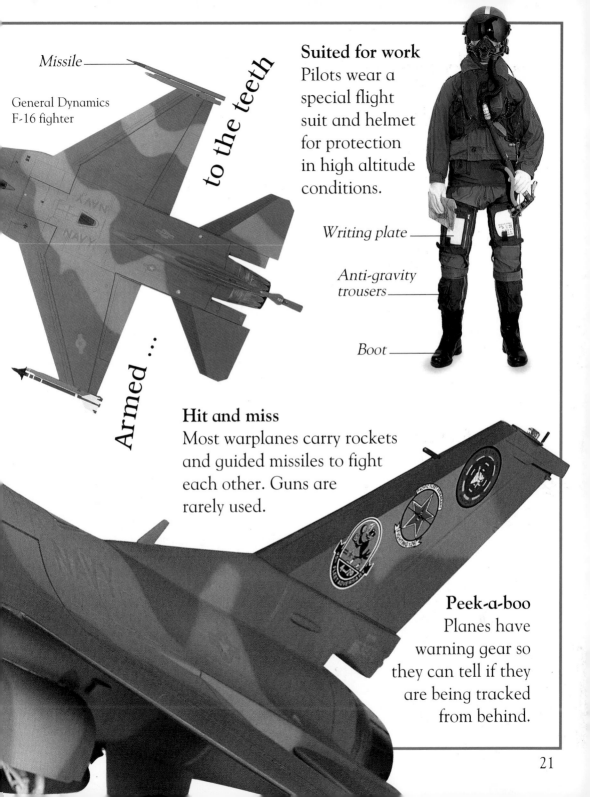

Missile ———

General Dynamics
F-16 fighter

to the teeth

Armed ...

Suited for work
Pilots wear a
special flight
suit and helmet
for protection
in high altitude
conditions.

Writing plate ———

*Anti-gravity
trousers* ———

Boot ———

Hit and miss
Most warplanes carry rockets
and guided missiles to fight
each other. Guns are
rarely used.

Peek-a-boo
Planes have
warning gear so
they can tell if they
are being tracked
from behind.

Light flight

Many people enjoy flying small, single-engine planes just for fun. They are light and easy to handle.

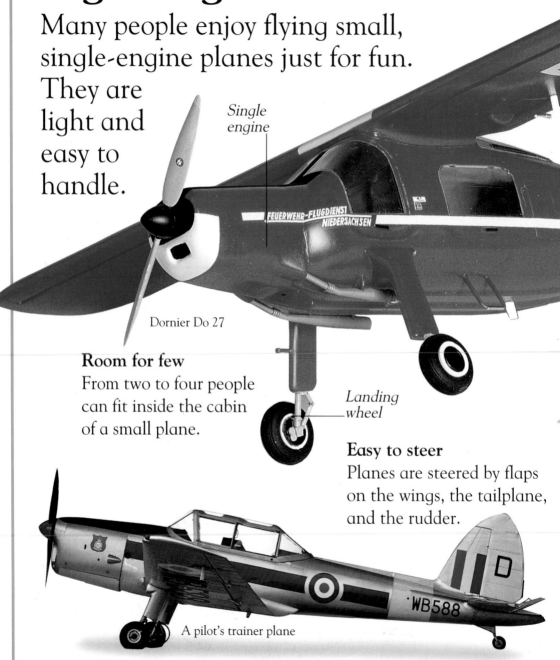

Single engine

Dornier Do 27

Room for few
From two to four people can fit inside the cabin of a small plane.

Landing wheel

Easy to steer
Planes are steered by flaps on the wings, the tailplane, and the rudder.

A pilot's trainer plane

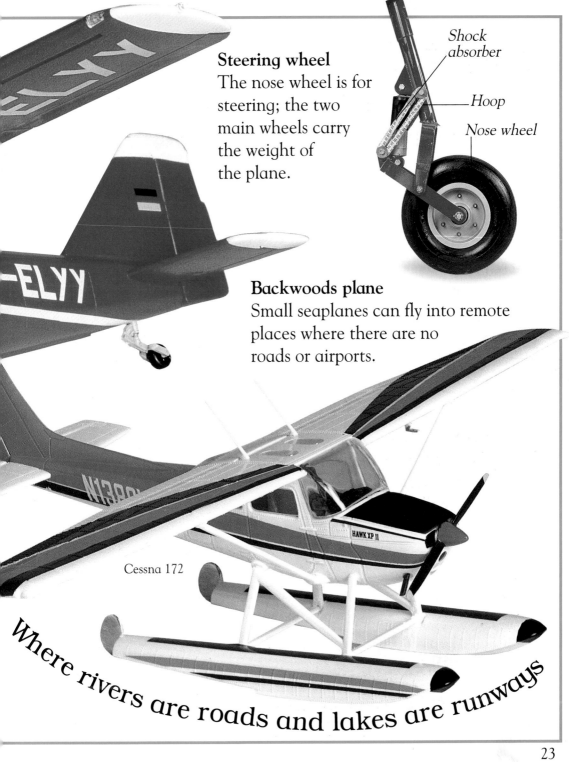

Steering wheel
The nose wheel is for steering; the two main wheels carry the weight of the plane.

Shock absorber

Hoop

Nose wheel

Backwoods plane
Small seaplanes can fly into remote places where there are no roads or airports.

Cessna 172

HAWK XP II

Where rivers are roads and lakes are runways

Fly like a bird

Just like birds that soar, gliders have
extra-long wings that lift them up
on even the gentlest
breezes.

Hardly more ...
than a giant kite with an engine

Slippery body
Without engine power, gliders
need streamlined bodies that
slip through the air and
a large wingspan (up to
about 25m or 82ft).

KI

Glider

Wing

The only way up is ...
by being towed

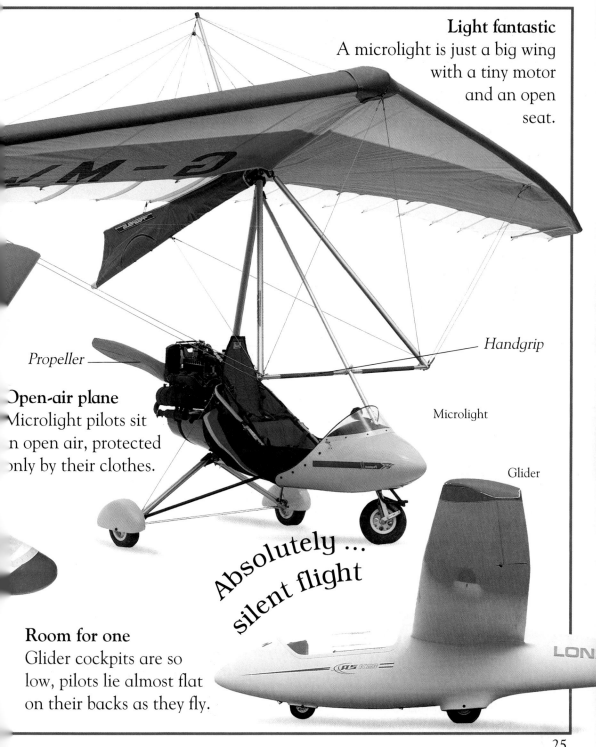

Light fantastic
A microlight is just a big wing with a tiny motor and an open seat.

Propeller

Handgrip

Open-air plane
Microlight pilots sit in open air, protected only by their clothes.

Microlight

Glider

Absolutely ... silent flight

Room for one
Glider cockpits are so low, pilots lie almost flat on their backs as they fly.

Faster than sound

Jets that fly faster than the speed of sound are called supersonic planes. Concorde is the only supersonic passenger jet in service today.

Most supersonic jets are military

BAC 221

A blue streak
Like all supersonic jets, the BAC-221 is long and pointed like a paper dart.

Concorde goes over twice as fast as other ...

BRITISH AIRWAYS

Thin fin
Concorde's body is narrow, and its wings and tail are thin to help it slip through the air at high speeds.

Emergency window

Flight deck windscreen

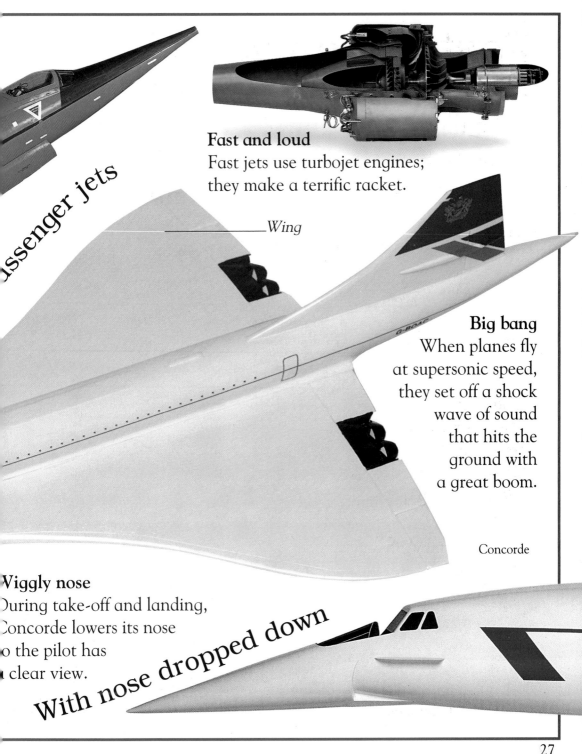

...ssenger jets

Fast and loud
Fast jets use turbojet engines;
they make a terrific racket.

Wing

Big bang
When planes fly
at supersonic speed,
they set off a shock
wave of sound
that hits the
ground with
a great boom.

Concorde

Wiggly nose
During take-off and landing,
Concorde lowers its nose
so the pilot has
a clear view.

With nose dropped down

On the job

Pilots fly in the cockpit, where controls for the engines, wings, and flaps are found. Other instruments show exactly where and how high the plane is flying.

The navigati display gives plane's locat.

60 years ago
In the early days of flight, cockpits had few instruments to help the pilots fly safely.

Pilots don't ...

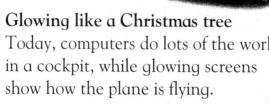

Glowing like a Christmas tree
Today, computers do lots of the work in a cockpit, while glowing screens show how the plane is flying.

The artificial horizon helps the plane stay level to the ground.

The direction finder shows the direction of the plane.

The flight display tells how high and fast the plane is flying.

need to look out the window to fly

Primary flight display

Loudspeaker

Co-pilot's pedal

Index

Five fiendish questions

1) Who first flew in a plane with an engine

2) What do you call a plane with three wings?

3) Which planes can swim like ducks?

4) A plane with no engine is called:
a) a slipper b) a glide
c) a crasher d) a sail

5) How many wings does a helicopter hav

Answers on page 32

Goes up like a lift

Hovers like a bee

Flies in any direction

Answers

From page 14-15: A seaplane lands on pontoons, a flying boat lands on its hull and an amphibian can land on water or land.

From page 30-31: 1. The Wright brothers
2. A triplane
3. Seaplanes
4. A glider
5. None, helicopters don't have wings